THE ART OF MINDFULNESS

PEACE AND CALM COLOURING

Michael O'Mara Books Limited

First published in Great Britain in 2015 by
Michael O'Mara Books Limited
9 Lion Yard
Tremadoc Road
London SW4 7NQ

A CIP catalogue record for this book is available from the British Library.

Papers used by Michael O'Mara Books Limited are natural, recyclable products made from wood grown in sustainable forests. The manufacturing processes conform to the environmental regulations of the country of origin.

ISBN: 978-1-78243-493-1

5 6 7 8 9 10

www.mombooks.com

Designed by Ana Bjezancevic and Claire Cater

Illustrations by Andrew Rowland, Angela Porter, Angelea Van Dam, Emily Hamilton, Felicity French, Hannah Davies, James Newman-Gray, Lizzie Preston, Mat Edwards, Rebecca Dinnage and Sally Moret

Cover illustration by Angelea Van Dam

Printed and bound in Germany

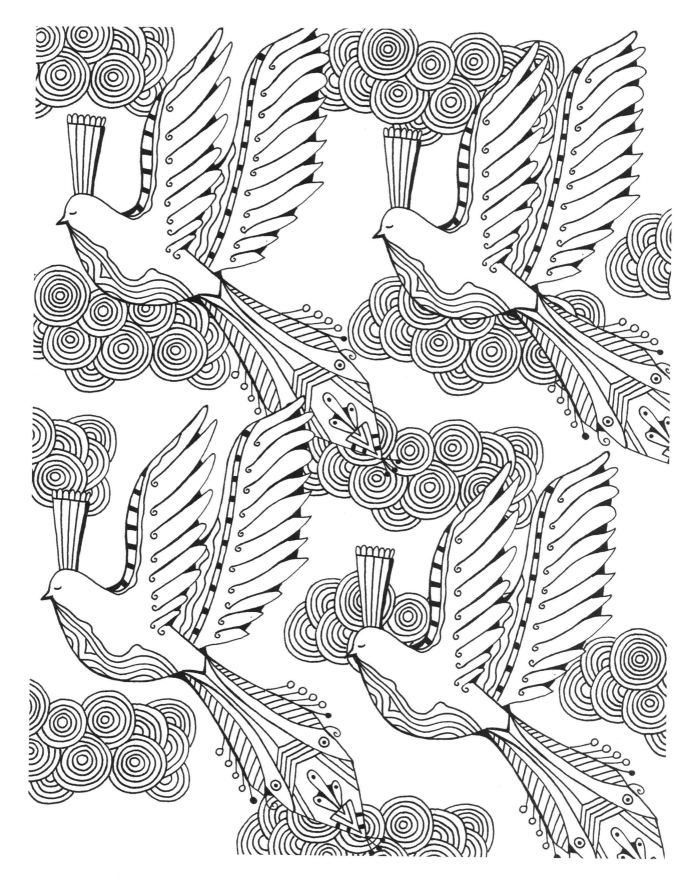

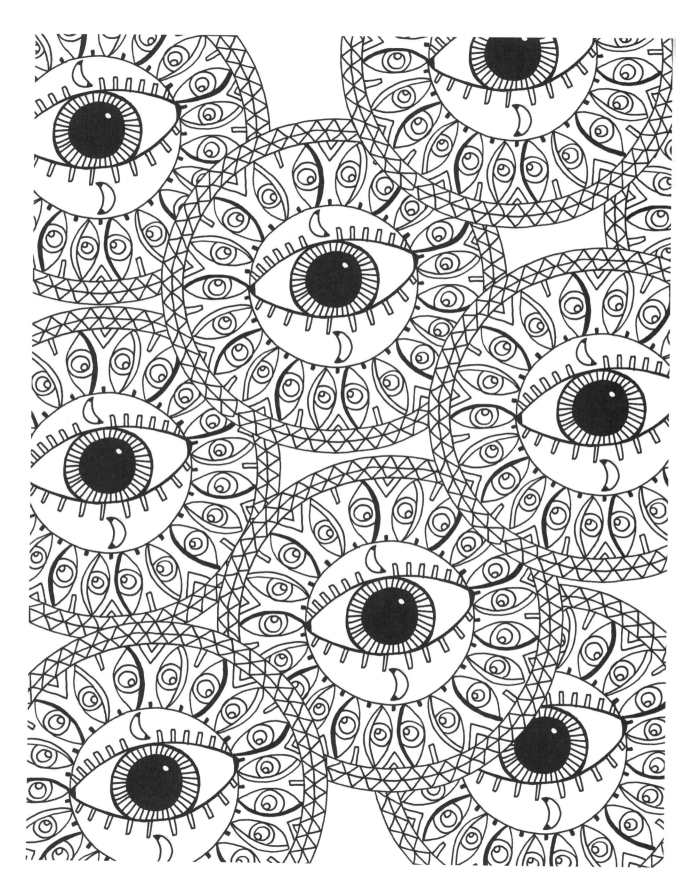

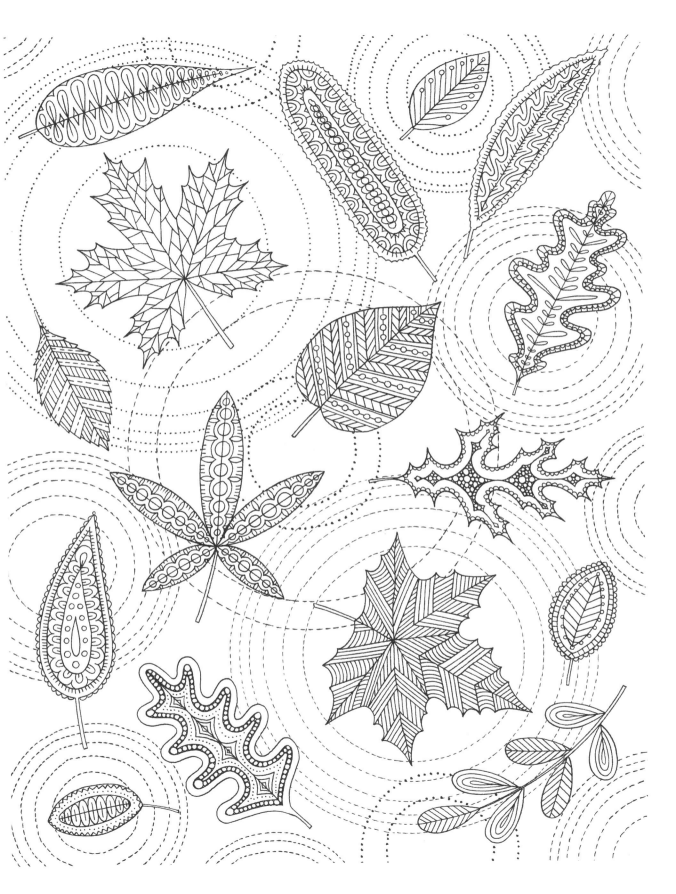

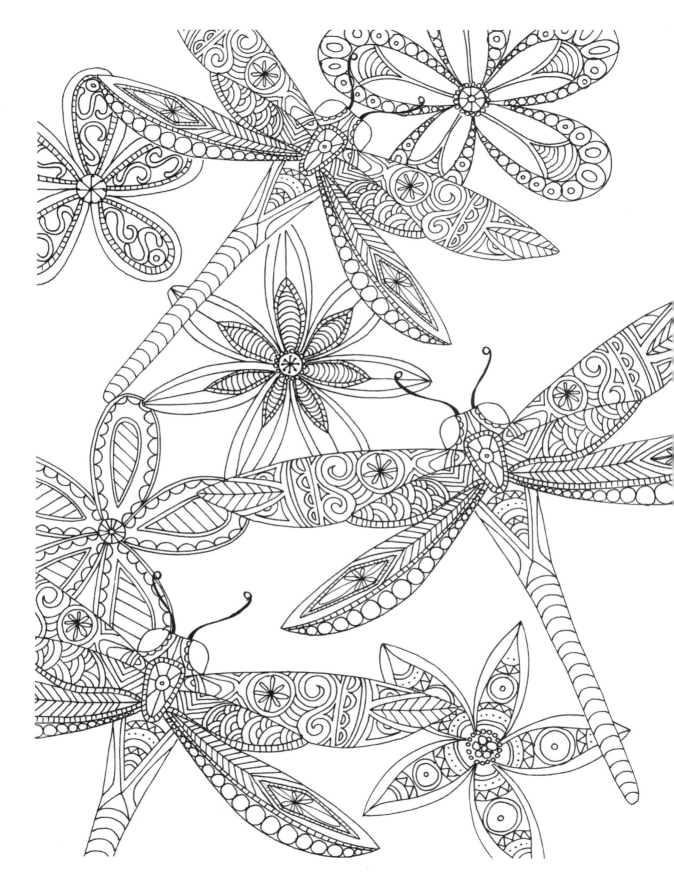

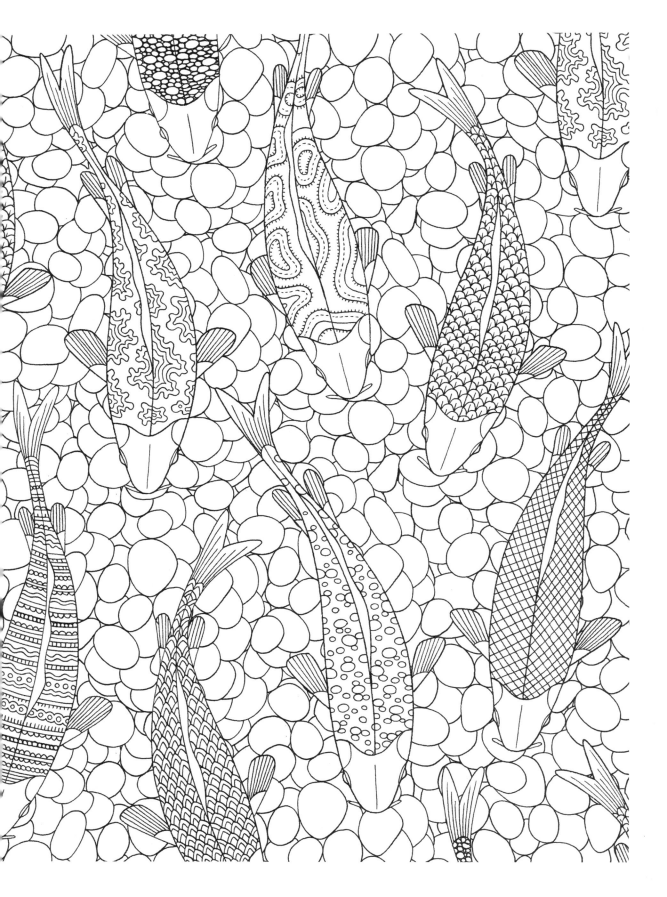